£6 10

Printed and Published in Great Britain by D. C. Thomson & Co., Ltd., 185 Fleet Street, London EC 4A 2HS.
© D. C. THOMSON & Co. Ltd. 2001.   ISBN 0 85116 776 4.

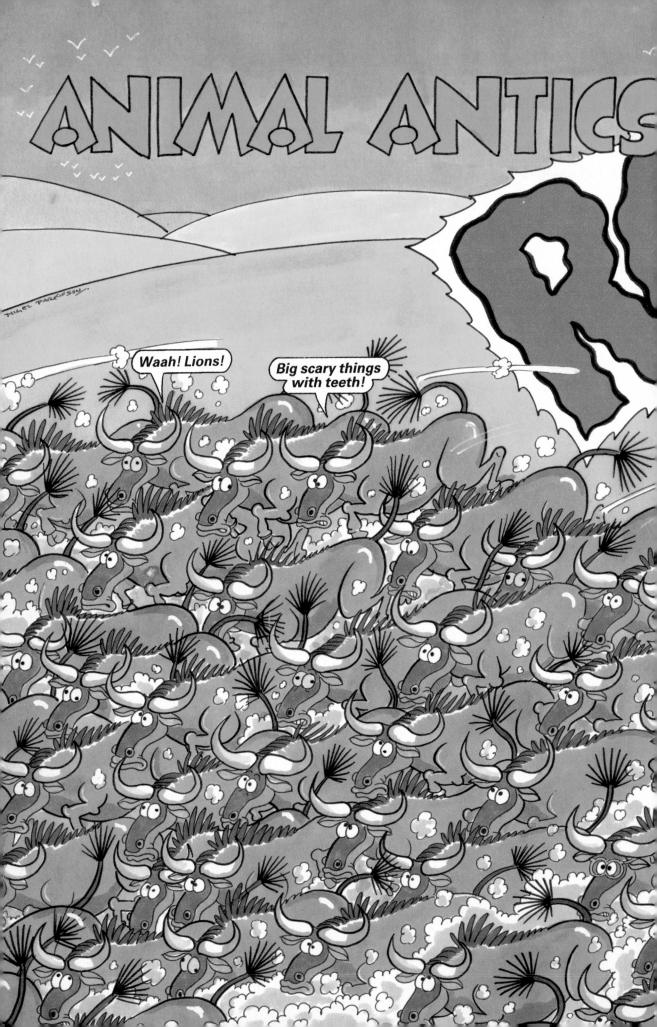

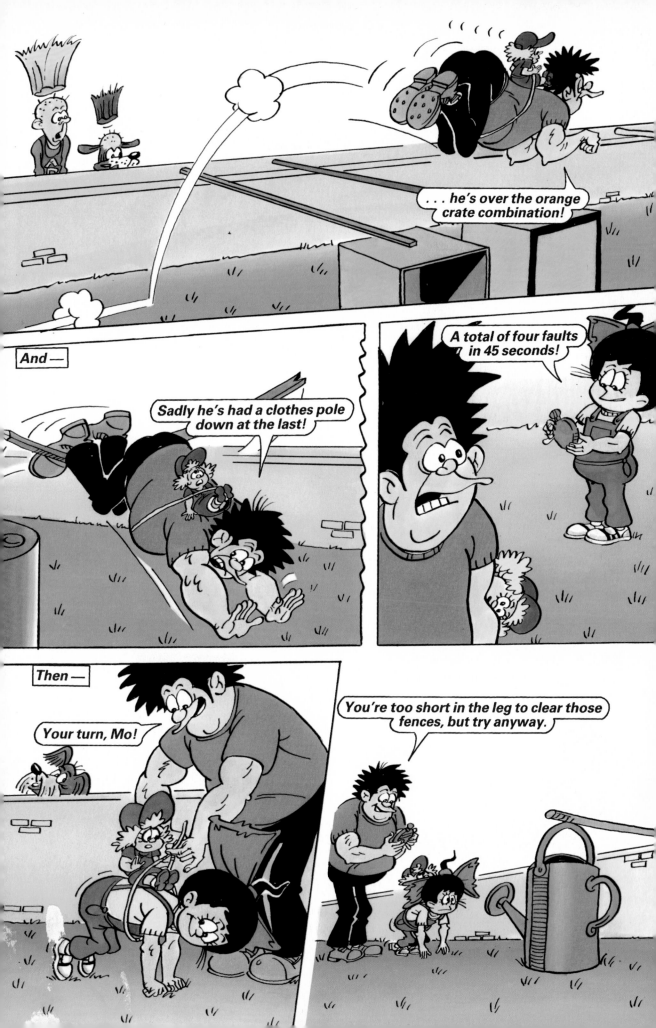

BABY CROCKETT

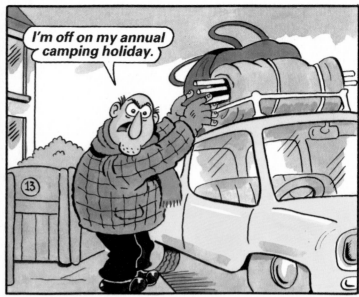

And —

It's the day we go to the Beezertown car boot sale!

VROOM!

So —

WHOOSH!

Mum was right!

How did we do?

We sold everything — right down to the spare wheel and a dead wasp that was on the parcel shelf!

A trendy Peruvian hat?

That's a tea cosy!

Aardvark repellent?

NEARLY SLEPT IN FOR MY WORK. TIME TO LOG ON.

THAT THING FROM MY DREAM- IT'S ON MY SCREEN!

THAT "THING" ROBBIE, I'VE SEEN BEFORE.

PROF. POTTER IS ROBBIE'S DEPARTMENT HEAD-

BACK IN THE 60's, THE JELLYMEN CROSSED BRITAIN, FROM THE NORTH SEA TO THE ATLANTIC!

SO IF THOSE JELLYMEN ARE ALL IN THE OCEAN, WHY AM I BEING HAUNTED BY ONE?

THEY WERE SAID TO HAVE THE POWER OF TELEPATHY. LET'S TRY A LITTLE EXPERIMENT.

ANIMAL ANTICS
Take your time and pick out the one who stole your pilchard!
BEEZERTOWN POLICE STATION
FUNNY ANIMAL DIVISION
WATCH OUT FOR PICKPOCKETS AND CHECK THOSE PELICANS' BILLS! YOU CAN HIDE A LOT IN ONE OF THEM!
6'
5'
4'
3'
2'
1'
1
2
3
4
5
IDENTITY PARADE
DO
POINT AT VILLAIN & SAY HIS NUMBER
DO NOT
RUN IN AND GIVE HIM A GOOD THUMPING!!
NIGEL PARKINSON

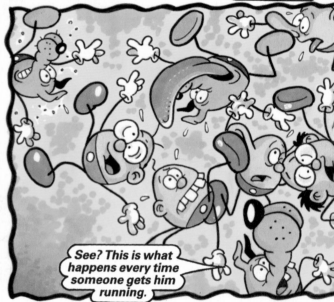

SMART ART

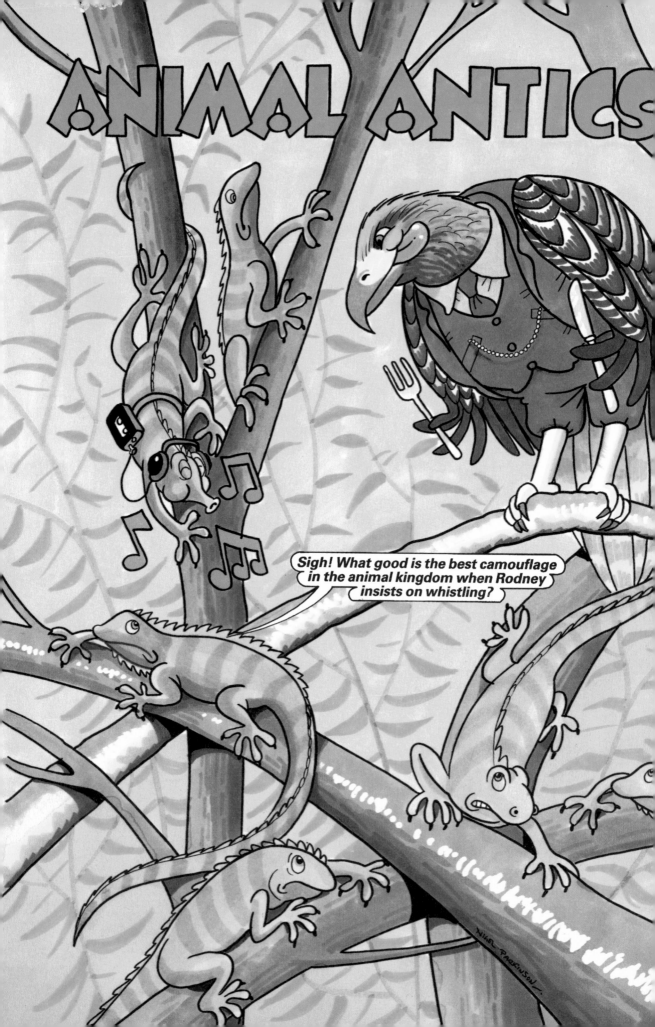

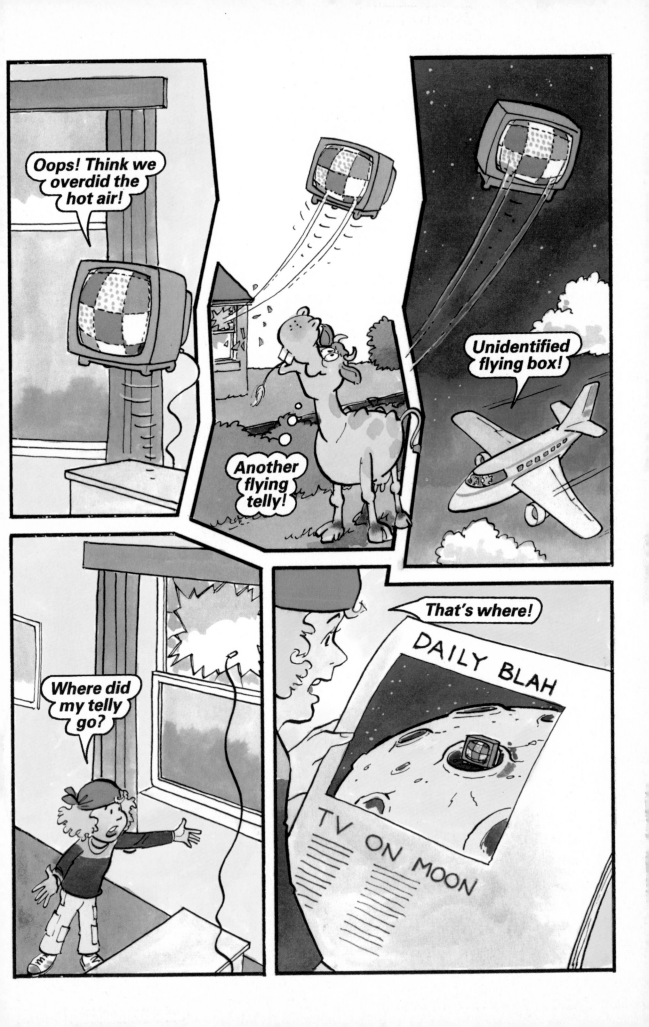

Desert Island DICK

KELLY

AND HIS ASSISTANT CEDRIC

Where's my magnifying glass? It keeps hiding from me.

In the laboratory of Professor Mad —

I have captured Agent Kelly's magnifying glass, and with it, I'll rule the world.

First I'll treat it with my mad laser beams.

Now, anything I look at will become magnified.

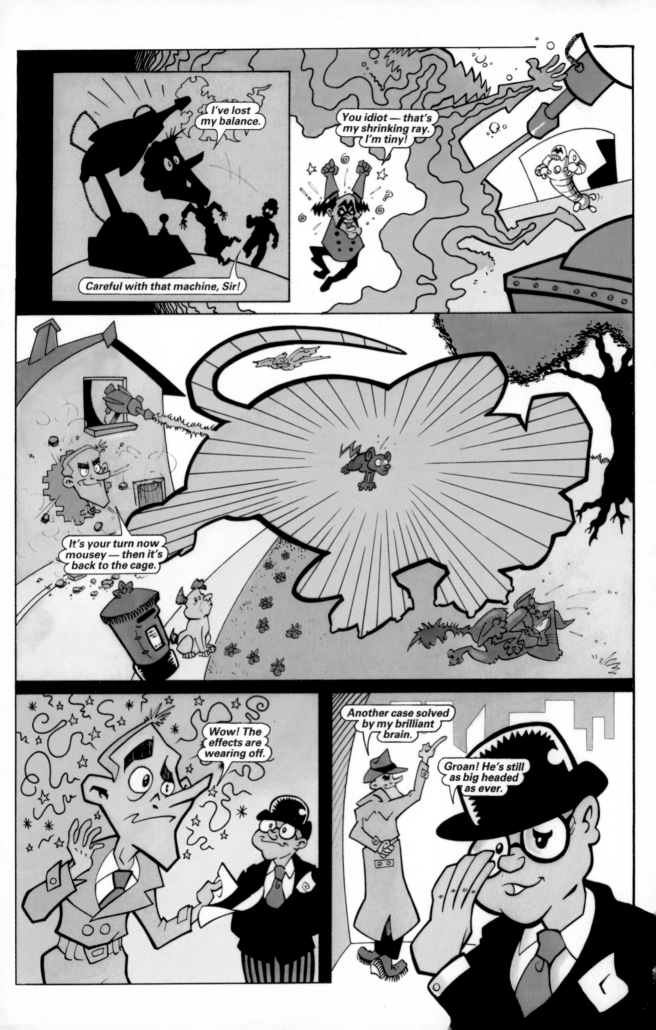

WILLY NiLLY

1

Willy Nilly is a boy with an unusual problem — his feet lead him off in weird and wonderful directions! A trip to the chip shop can easily find him in the foothills of the Andes or a walk to school can end up on the sweeping vista of an Arctic tundra. Since llamas don't normally sell fish suppers and Pythagoras' theorem is not taught by your average yak, Willy's freewheeling feet often landed him in trouble.

3

The finest doctors in the land had examined Willy's well-travelled tootsies and could find nothing wrong with them. The worst doctors in the land also had a look and were equally bamboozled, although one of them did suggest that Wellington boots fitted with a built-in satellite navigation system might help Willy's problem. The 3 million dollar asking price for such fabulous footwear was outwith the Nilly family budget and Willy's exasperated Mum decided keeping him indoors would be a cheaper and more effective solution.

5

The two wanderers eagerly exchanged messages and photographs and true love blossomed. They decided to sneak out of their respective houses and meet up in the town square. With the frivolous nature of their feet, however, this plan was doomed to failure.

2

A great football fan, Willy, not surprisingly, supported Bolton Wanderers but had never seen them play. In their last cup-tie against Manchester United, he missed Old Trafford by some 12,000 miles and ended up on Easter Island!

4

Stuck in his room, the lonely Willy turned to the internet to brighten up what had now become an exceedingly dull life. He scanned the chat rooms, hoping to find someone with feet as unpredictable as his own. That was how he encountered the love of his young life — Dilly Dally. Dilly was also confined to her house (a trip to post a letter had resulted in a raft trip down the Euphrates river).

6

Willy found himself in downtown New York and Dilly ended up on the Clifton suspension bridge. The pair were heartbroken.

7

After failing to meet up on a further 27 different occasions Willy Nilly and Dilly Dally decided to go their separate ways. Tearfully, Willy packed his bags for a trip to Bangladesh while a sobbing Dilly set off for Alice Springs in the Australian outback.

8

Love, they say, conquers all and this unique romance did have a happy ending. Willy's feet never reached Bangladesh and he ended up in the local swingpark — at exactly the same time as Dilly Dally's visit to Alice Springs arrived at the climbing frame! They hugged, they kissed, there was joy in the air. Aw! That night Willy walked his girlfriend to her home in Green Street — by way of the Taj Mahal, the Gobi desert, Barbados, Lake Superior . . .

THE END

MYSTERY OF THE MIDNIGHT MANSION

JESSICA AND JOSH WERE ON HOLIDAY AT THEIR AUNT'S FARM IN THE COUNTRYSIDE.

ARE YOU SURE THIS IS THE RIGHT PLACE, JESS? IT LOOKS KIND OF SPOOKY.

WHAT? OH, DON'T BE SUCH A BIG KID.

IT'S ALL IN AUNT VICKY'S NOTE, SEE? BIG HOUSE, JUST OVER THE FIELDS . . . THIS MUST BE IT.

Dear J & J,
I've gone to visit Mrs Jenkins. If you need anything she lives at the big house just over the fields.
Love,
Aunt Vicky.

COME ON! WHAT ARE YOU SCARED OF? DRACULA?

MIDNIGHT MANSION

ULP! 'MIDNIGHT MANSION'? WHAT KIND OF NAME IS THAT?

HELLO? MRS JENKINS? AUNTIE VICKY . . . ? FUNNY. THE LIGHTS ARE ON BUT NOBODY'S HOME.

I'VE BEEN SAYING THAT ABOUT YOU FOR YEARS.

THE TEDDY BEAR WAS NAMED AFTER U.S. PRESIDENT THEODORE "TEDDY" ROOSEVELT. HE STARTED THE FASHION FOR BEARS WHEN ADOPTING ONE AS A PET DURING A HUNTING TRIP TO THE ROCKIES.

AN ALERT BROOKLYN STATIONER BEGAN IMMEDIATELY TO MANUFACTURE TOY BEARS AND WROTE TO THE PRESIDENT FOR PERMISSION TO USE THE NAME "TEDDYS".

ROOSEVELT REPLIED: "I DON'T THINK MY NAME IS LIKELY TO BE WORTH MUCH IN THE BEAR BUSINESS, BUT YOU ARE WELCOME TO USE IT."

CREATURES

AT CEDAR LAKE INDIANA, A 100 LB WATCHDOG LOOKED ON IMPASSIVELY WHILE TWO MEN RAIDED HIS MASTER'S BUSINESS PREMISES.

THEN HE BIT THE POLICEMAN CALLED TO INVESTIGATE.

THE GABOON VIPER HAS THE LONGEST FANGS OF ANY SNAKE. THE SPECIMEN KEPT IN THE PHILADELPHIA ZOO IN 1963 WAS A LITTLE CARELESS AND BIT ITSELF TO DEATH!

THE LONGEST AND HEAVIEST OF ALL SNAKES IS THE ANACONDA OF SOUTH AMERICA. SPECIMENS AS HEAVY AS 950 POUNDS AND AS LONG AS 38 FEET HAVE BEEN REPORTED.

A BABY RATTLESNAKE AT BIRTH HAS THE SAME AMOUNT OF POISONOUS VENOM AS A FULLY-GROWN RATTL